piano-vocal/easy piano-easy organ

Carole King Tapestry

D1872166

Printed by The Panda Group · Haverhill · Suffolk CB9 8PR · UK
Binding by ABS · Cambridge

so far away

By Carole King

So far away!
Doesn't anybody stay in one place anymore?
It would be so fine to see your face at my door.
Doesn't help to know you're just time away.
Long ago I reached for you and there you stood.
Holding you again could only do me good.
How I wish I could, but you're so far away!
One more song about movin' along the highway,
Can't say much of anything that's new.
If I could only work this life out my way,
I'd rather spend it bein' close to you,
But you're so far away!
Doesn't anybody stay in one place anymore?
It would be so fine to see your face at my door.
Doesn't help to know you're just time away.
Yeah, you're so far away!
Travelin' around sure gets me down and lonely.
Nothin' else to do but close my mind.
I sure hope the road don't come to own me.
There's so many dreams I've yet to find.
But you're so far away!
Doesn't anybody stay in one place anymore?

So Far Away

Words and Music by
CAROLE KING

Dmaj9 D6 Dmaj9 D6 Gmaj7 G6
time a - way. Long a-go I reached for you and there you stood.
Em7 G (A Bass) Dmaj7 (D Bass) G Dmaj7
Hold - ing you a - gain could on - ly do me good.
Gmaj7 F♯m7 Em7 (A Bass) G Dmaj9 D6 Dmaj9 D A (C♯ Bass)
How I wish I could, but you're so far a - way!
Bm A6 G D (F♯ Bass)
One more song a - bout mov- in' a - long the high-way

Em7
G
(A Bass)
Dmaj7
can't say much of an - y - thing that's new. If
F♯m
F♯m7
Em7
I could on - ly work this life out my way, I'd
G
(A Bass)
Bm
G
(E Bass)
G
(A Bass)
Dmaj9
D6
rath-er spend it be-in' close to you, but you're so far a - way!
Dmaj9
D6
Gmaj7
G6
Does-n't an-y-bod - y stay in one place an - y - more?

Em7 G (A Bass) Dmaj7 (D Bass) G Dmaj7
It would be so fine to see your face at my door. It
Gmaj7 F♯m7 Em7 G (A Bass) Dmaj9 D6
does-n't help to know you're so far a - way.
Dmaj9 D6 Gmaj7 G6 Em7 G (A Bass)
Yeah, you're so far a - way!
G (A Bass) A6 G (A Bass)
Trav-el - in' a - round sure gets me down and lone - ly.

Em7
G
(A Bass)
Dmaj7
Noth-in' else to do but close my mind. I
F♯m7
Em7
sure hope the road don't come to own me. There's
G
(A Bass)
Bm
Em7
G
(A Bass)
so man-y dreams I've yet to find. But you're so
Dmaj9
D6
Dmaj9
D6
far a - way! Does -n't an - y - bod - y stay in one place

Gmaj7
G6
Em7
G
(A Bass)
an - y - more? It would be so fine to see your
(D Bass)
Dmaj7
G
Dmaj7
Gmaj7
F♯m7
Em7
G
(A Bass)
face at my door, and it does-n't help to know you're so
Dmaj9
D6
Dmaj7
D6
Gmaj7
G6
far a - way! Yeah, you're so far a - way!
Em7
G
(A Bass)
Dmaj9
D6
Dmaj9
D6
Hey, you're so far a - way!

Gmaj7
G6
Em7
G
(A Bass)
3
Dmaj9
D6
Dmaj9
D6
Gmaj7
Em7
G
(A Bass)
Dmaj9
D6
Dmaj9
D6
Gmaj7
Em7
G
(A Bass)
Dmaj9
D6
On Repeat
Dmaj9
D6
Repeat and Fade

So Far Away

Words and Music by
CAROLE KING

Gm7 C11 Dm Gm7 C11 F
my way, I'd rath-er spend it be-in' close to you. But you're so far a-way!
Bb Gm7 C11 F Bb F
Does-n't an-y-bod-y stay in one place an-y more? It would be so fine to see your face at my door.
Bb Am7 Gm7 C11 F F Bb
Does-n't help to know you're just time a-way. Yeah, you're so far a-way.
Gm C9 Bb F Gm Bb
Trav-el-lin' a-round sure gets me down and lone-ly.
Gm7 C11 F Am
Noth-in' else to do but close my mind. I sure hope the road don't come to
Gm7 C11 Dm Gm7 C11
own me. There's so man-y dreams I've yet to find. But you're so
D. S. and fade

it's too late

By Toni Stern

Stayed in bed all mornin' just to pass the time.
There's somethin' wrong here,
There can be no denyin',
One of us is changin' or maybe
We've just stopped tryin'.
And it's too late, baby, now, it's too late.
Though we really did try to make it.
Somethin' inside has died
And I can't hide and I just can't fake it.
It used to be so easy living here with you;
You were light and breezy
And I knew just what to do.
Now you look so unhappy
And I feel like a fool.
And it's too late, baby, now it's too late,
Though we really did try to make it.
Somethin' inside has died
And I can't hide and I just can't fake it.
There'll be good times again for me and you;
But we just can't stay together
Don't you feel it, too?
Still I'm glad for what we had
And how I once loved you.
And it's too late, baby, now it's too late,
Though we really did try to make it.
Somethin' inside has died
And I can't hide and I just can't fake it.
It's too late, baby, it's too late now,
Darlin', it's too late.

It's Too Late

Words by TONI STERN
Music by CAROLE KING

Moderately Slow

Gm7
Fmaj7
may- be we've just stopped try - in'.
feel like a fool.
And it's too
mf
B♭maj7
Fmaj7
B♭maj7
late, ba - by now, it's too late, though we real -ly did try to make
Fmaj7
B♭maj7
Fmaj7
it.
Some-thin' in - side has died, and I can't hide.

Dm7
1. Esus
Em7
Am7
D6
and I just can't fake it, oh, no, no.
Am7
D6
It
Ped.
2. F (G Bass)
G7
Cmaj7
Fmaj7
it, oh, no, no.
(after D.S.) no, no, no, no.

Bbmaj7
Am7
Gm7
Fmaj7
Dm7
To Coda
E7sus
E7
Am7
D6
Play twice - then repeat as desired for ad lib. solos.
Am7
Dm6
When ready play this section twice and continue.
Am7
D6
There'll be good times a - gain for
Am7
D6
me and you, but we just can't stay to-geth- er; don't you feel it too? Still I'm

Am7
Gm7
Fmaj7
glad for what we had and how I once loved you.
D.S. al Coda
(use 2nd ending)
But it's too
mf
Coda
F
(G Bass)
G7
It's too late,
Cmaj7
Fmaj7
Cmaj7
Fmaj7
baby, it's too late now, dar-
Cmaj9
lin', it's too late.

It's Too Late

Words by TONI STERN
Music by CAROLE KING

i feel the earth move

By Carole King

I feel the earth move under my feet;
I feel the sky tumbling down;
I feel my heart start to tremblin'
Whenever you're around, Ooh, baby,
When I see your face
Mellow as the month of May,
Oh, darlin', I can't stand it
When you look at me that way.
I feel the earth move under my feet;
I feel the sky tumblin' down;
I feel my heart start to tremblin'
Whenever you're around, Ooh, darlin'
When I'm near you
And you tenderly call my name,
I know that my emotions
Are something I just can't tame.
I just got to have you, baby.
Ah! Ah! Yes,
I feel the earth move under my feet;
I feel the sky tumblin' down,
Tumblin' down.

I Feel The Earth Move

Words and Music by
CAROLE KING

1.
Dm7 (C Bass)
Ab (Bb Bass)
Ebmaj7
Fm
Gm
Abmaj7
Ooh, ba - by, when I see your face,
Fm7
Ab (Bb Bass)
Ebmaj7
Fm
Gm
Abmaj7
mel-low as the month of May, oh, dar - lin', I can't stand
Fm7
Ab (Bb Bass)
F (G Bass)
it when you look at me that (-a) way. I feel the
2.
Dm7 (C Bass)
Cm7
F6

Cm7
F
(C Bass)
Cm7
F7
Cm7
F
(C Bass)
Cm7
F7
Cm7
(add F no D)
F9
Cm7
F7
3
Cm7
F7
Cm7

F7
Ab
(Bb Bass)
Ebmaj7
Abmaj7
Ooh, dar - lin', when you're near me and you ten -
Fm7
Ab
(Bb Bass)
Ebmaj7
Fm
Gm
Abmaj7
der - ly call my name, I know that my e - mo -
Fm7
Ab
(Bb Bass)
F
(G Bass)
tions are some-thing I just can't tame. I've just got to have you
Cm7
(C Bass)
F
Cm7
(C Bass)
F
Cm7
ba - by. Ah, ah, ah, ah, ah, ah, yeah!

(C Bass) F
Cm7
(C Bass) F
Cm7
F (C Bass)
I feel the earth move under my feet; I feel the
Cm7
F (C Bass)
Cm7
sky tum-bl-in' down, a - tum-bl - in' down. I feel the earth move un -
F (C Bass)
Cm7
To Coda
F (C Bass)
der my feet; I feel the sky tum-bl - in' down, a -tum-bl - in' down. I just (-a)
Cm7
F7
Cm7
lose con-trol, down to my ver - y soul.

F7
Cm7
F7
I get (-a) hot and cold all o-
Cm7
F (C Bass)
D.S.al Coda
ver, all o - ver, all o - ver, all o - ver. I feel the
p
mf
f
Dm7 (C Bass)
Cm7
-tum- bl - in' down, a - tum - bl - in' down, a - tum - bl - in' down,
Coda
rit
B♭maj7 (C Bass)
A♭maj7 (C Bass)
B♭maj7 (C Bass)
a- tum-bl - in'down, tum-bl- in' down.
Gradually
Ped.

I Feel The Earth Move

Words and Music by
CAROLE KING

G
I feel my heart start to trem-bl-in' whenev-er
Dm7 G Dm7 G C7
you're a-round. Ooh,
F Bb Gm7 C9
dar-lin', when I'm near you And you ten-der-ly call my name, I
F Bb Gm C9 A7
know that my e-mo-tions Are some-thing I just can't tame. I just got to have you
Dm7 G7 Dm7 G
ba-by. Ah! Ah! Yes, I feel the
Repeat and fade
Dm7 G Dm7 G
earth move un-der my feet; I feel the sky tum-bl-in' down, tum-bl-in' down. I feel the

home again

By Carole King

Sometimes I wonder if
I'm ever gonna make it home again,
It's so far and out of sight.
I really need someone to talk to
And nobody else knows how to
Comfort me tonight.
Snow is cold, rain is wet;
Chills my soul right to the marrow.
I won't be happy till I see you alone again,
Till I'm home again and feelin' right
Snow is cold, rain is wet;
Chills my soul right to the marrow.
I won't be happy till I see you alone again,
Till I'm home again and feelin' right.
Till I'm home again and feelin' right.
I wanna be home again and feelin' right.

Home Again

Words and Music by
CAROLE KING

A (C♯ Bass)
Bm7
A
D (A Bass)
A
and out of sight.
I real - ly
E (A Bass)
D (A Bass)
A
need some - one to talk to, and no - bod - y else
D
A (C♯ Bass)
Bm7
A
knows how to com - fort me to - night.
R.H.
F♯m
A7
Snow is cold, rain is wet;
mf
3

D
A (C# Bass)
B7sus
B7
(E Bass) Bm7
E7
chills my soul right to the mar - row.
R.H
A
(A Bass) E
I won't be hap - py till I see you a - lone
D (A Bass)
A
D
A (C# Bass)
Bm7
Bm7 (E Bass)
a - gain, till I'm home a - gain and feel - - in'
R.H.
A
NC
G (A Bass)
D (A Bass)
A
NC
G (A Bass)
D (A Bass)
right.

A
E (A Bass)
D (A Bass)
Bm7
A
D
G
D
A
D (A Bass)
R.H
Ped.
A
(A Bass)
E
(A Bass)
D
A
D
G
D
A
Ped.

F♯m
A7
Snow is cold, rain is wet;
D
A (C♯ Bass)
B7sus
B7
Bm7 (E Bass)
E7
chills my soul right to the mar - row.
A
E (A Bass)
D
A
I won't be hap - py till I see you a - lone a - gain,
mp
D
A (C♯ Bass)
Bm7
(E Bass) D
A
(A Bass) D
A
till I'm home a-gain and feel - in' right;
mf
R.H.

D
A (C♯ Bass)
Bm7
D (E Bass)
A
till I'm home a-gain and feel - in' right.
D (A Bass)
D
Ped.
A (C♯ Bass)
Bm7
D (E Bass)
I wan - na be home a-gain and feel - in'
A
NC
(A Bass) G
D (A Bass)
A
NC
(A Bass) G
right.
D (A Bass)
A
NC
(A Bass) G
(A Bass) D
A

Home Again

Words and Music by
CAROLE KING

way over yonder

By Carole King

'Way over yonder is a place that I know
Where I can find shelter from hunger and cold
And the sweet tastin' good life is so easily found.
'Way over yonder, that's where I'm bound.
I know when I get there the first thing I'll see
Is the sun shinin' golden, shinin' right down on me.
Then trouble's gonna lose me, worry leave me behind
And I'll stand up proudly in true peace of mind.
Talkin' 'bout a, talkin' 'bout away over yonder
Is a place I have seen. It's a garden of wisdom
From some long ago dream.
Maybe tomorrow I'll find my way
To the land where the honey runs in rivers each day.
And the sweet tastin' good life is so easily found.
'Way over yonder, that's where I'm bound.

Way Over Yonder

Words and Music by
CAROLE KING

Dm7
(G Bass)
C
F
F
(E Bass)
F
(D Bass)
from hun - ger and cold.
in riv - ers each day.
C
(B Bass)
(B♭ Bass)
A7sus
And the sweet tast-in' good life is so eas-
Dm7
Dm7
(G Bass)
i - ly found.
'Way ov - er
F
F
(G Bass)
C
to Coda
yon - der, that's where I'm bound.

F
C
(E Bass)
Dm7
G7
C
C
(C Bass)
I know when I get there,
C
C
(B Bass)
C
(A Bass)
G
the first thing I'll see
G7
Dm7
Dm7
(G Bass)
is the sun shin-ing gold - en, shin - in'
C
F
(C Bass)
C
right down on me. Then

C (B Bass)
C (B♭ Bass)
A7sus
trou - ble's gon - na lose me, wor - ry
Dm7
leave me be - hind, and I'll stand up
C (G Bass)
Dm7 (G Bass)
F (C Bass)
proud - ly in true peace of mind.
C (E Bass)
Dm7
Dm7 (G Bass)
Talk - in' 'bout a, talk - in' 'bout a - way ov - er yon -

F (G Bass) C C (B Bass) Am
der is a place I have seen.
Dm Dm7
It's a gar - den of wis-dom
Dm7 (G Bass) C C (B Bass) Am
from some long a - go dream.
G9 Dm7 (G Bass)
D.S. 𝄋 al ⊕ Coda
May - be to -
Coda
F C (E Bass) Dm C
Fine

Way Over Yonder

Words and Music by
CAROLE KING

C7 Gm7 Gm7/C F
Is the sun shin-in' gold - en, shin -in' right down on me.
B♭ F D7sus 3
Then trou-ble's gon -na lose me, wor - ry leave me be -
Gm7 F
hind And I'll stand up proud - ly
Gm7/C B♭ F Gm7 Gm7/C F B♭ F
in true peace of mind. Talk-in' 'bout a, talk-in' 'bout a - way o-ver yon - der is a
Dm Gm7
place I have seen. It's a gar - den of wis - dom
Gm7 C F C7 Gm7/C D. S. al Fine
from some long a - go dream. May - be to -

you've got a friend

By Carole King

When you're down and troubled
and yu need some love and care
And nothin', nothin' is goin' right,
Close your eyes and think of me
And soon I will be there to
Brighten up even your darkest night.
You just call out my name
And you know whenever I am
I'll come runnin' to see you again.
Winter, spring, summer or fall
All you have to do is call
And I'll be there. You've got a friend.
If the sky above you
Grows dark and full of clouds
And that ol' north wind begins to blow,
Keep your head together
And call my name out loud;
Soon you'll hear me knockin' at your door.
You just call out my name
And you know wherever I am
I'll come runnin' to see you again.
Winter, spring, summer or fall
Al you have to do is call
And I'll be there, yes, I will.
Now ain't it good to know
That you've got a friend
When people can be so cold?
They'll hurt you, yes, and desert you
And take your soul if you let them.
Oh, but don't you let them.
You just call out my name
And you know wherever I am
I'll come runnin' to see you again.
Winter, spring, summer or fall
All you have to do is call
And I'll be there, yes, I will.
You've got a friend. You've got a friend
Ain't it good to know you've got a friend

You've Got A Friend

Words and Music by
CAROLE KING

Slowly, with expression

Eb7
Ab
nothin' is go - in' right;
be - gins to blow;
Gm7
C7
Fm
C7
close your eyes and think of me and soon I will be there
keep your head to - geth - er and call my name out loud;
Fm
C7
Fm
Bbm7
Cm7
to bright-en up e - ven your dark - est night.
Soon you'll hear me knock- in' at your door.
Db6
(Eb Bass)
Eb
Db6
(Eb Bass)
Ab
You just call out my name
mf

D♭
and you know wher-ev-er I am, I'll come run-
A♭
D♭6
(E♭ Bass)
nin' to see you a - gain.
A♭
Win-ter, spring, sum-mer or fall,
D♭
A♭6
A♭7
to Coda
all you have to do is call, and I'll be

D♭
Cm7
B♭m7
D♭6
(E♭ Bass)
A♭
1.
there.
You've got a friend.
D♭
(A♭ Bass)
D♭
A♭(C Bass)
B♭m
A♭
(C Bass)
A♭
Gm7
C
(N. C.)
2. If the sky
D♭
Cm7
B♭m7
D♭6
(E♭ Bass)
G♭
D♭
2.
there, yes, I will.
Now ain't it good to know that you've
A♭
A♭maj7
got a friend when peo-ple can be so cold?
They'll hurt

D♭
G♭7
Fm
you, yes, and de-sert you and take your soul if you let
B♭7
B♭m7
(E♭ Bass)
D.S. 𝄋 al ⊕ Coda
them. Oh, but don't you let them. You just call
⊕ Coda
D♭
Cm
B♭m7
D♭6
(E♭ Bass)
A♭
there, yes, I will. You've got a friend.
D♭
(A♭ Bass)
A♭
D♭
Repeat and fade
You've got a friend. Ain't it good to know you've got a

You've Got A Friend

Words and Music by
CAROLE KING

C
run-nin'
to see you a-gain.
F6/G
C
Win-ter, spring, sum-mer or
fall
F
All you have to do is call
C
C7
And I'll
F
Em
be there.
1.
Dm7
G11
You've got a
C
friend.
If the sky
2.
To next strain
Dm7
G11
Now
3.
Fine
Dm7
G11
You've got a
C
friend.
B♭
ain't it good to know that you've
F
got a friend
When
C
peo-ple can be so
cold?
They'll
F
hurt you, yes, and de-
B♭7
sert you.
And
Am
take your soul if you let
D9
them. Oh, but
F/G
don't you let them.
You just call
D. S. al Fine

will you love me tomorrow?

By Gerry Goffin and Carole King

Tonight you're mine completely;
You give your love so sweetly;
Tonight the light of love is in your eyes,
But will you love me tomorrow?
Is this a lasting treasure
Or just a moment's pleasure?
Can I believe the magic of your sighs?
Will you still love me tomorrow?
Tonight, with words unspoken;
You say that I'm the only one;
But will my heart be broken
When the night meets the morning sun?
I have to know that your love
Is love I can be sure of.
So, tell me now and I won't ask again,
Will you still love me tomorrow?
Will you still love me tomorrow?

Will You Love Me Tomorrow?

Words and Music by
GERRY GOFFIN and CAROLE KING

Esus
E
Am
E
(G♯ Bass)
Am
the light of love is in your eyes,
be - lieve the mag - ic of your sighs?
Am7
(G Bass)
F
G
but will you love me to - mor -
Will you still love me to - mor -
C
Dm7
1. (G Bass)
2.
Gm7
C7
row?
row?
F
Em
To - night with words un - spok - en,

F
F
(G Bass)
you say that I'm the on - ly one;
C
C7
F
But will my
Em
heart be brok - en
when the night
Am
D
Dm7
meets the morn- ing sun?

G
C
I'd like to know that your
F
F
(G Bass)
C
love is the love I can
F
(G Bass)
G
be sure of. So
3
3
E7sus
E7
Am
tell me now, and I won't ask a - gain.

G
F
G
Will you still love — me to - mor -
C
C7
F
row? —
Will you still
G
C
love — me to - mor - row?
F6
Dm7
(G Bass)
C
F
(G Bass)
C

Will You Love Me Tomorrow?

Words and Music by
GERRY GOFFIN and CAROLE KING

beautiful

By Carole King

You've got to get up ev'ry mornin'
With a smile on your face and show the world
All the love in your heart.
Then people gonna treat you better.
You're gonna find, yes, you will,
That you're beautiful as you feel.
Waiting at the station
With a workday wind a-blowing,
I've got nothing to do
But watch the passers by.
Mirrored in their faces I see frustration growing
And they don't see it showing, why I do?
You've go to get up ev'ry mornin'
With a smile on your face and show the world
All the love in your heart.
Then people gonna treat you better.
You're gonna find, yes, you will,
That you're beautiful as you feel.
I have often asked myself the reason
For the sadness in a world
Where tears are just a lullaby.
If there's any answer maybe love can end the madness.
Maybe not, oh, but we can only try.
You've got to get up ev'ry mornin'
With a smile on your face and show the world
All the love in your heart.
Then people gonna treat you better.
You're gonna find, yes, you will,
That you're beautiful, you're beautiful,
You're beautiful as you feel.

Beautiful

Words and Music by
CAROLE KING

Moderately Slow (In Two)

Eb (Bb Bass)
ter. You're gon-na find, yes, you will, that you're beau-
To Coda
Eb (Bb Bass)
- ti - ful as you feel.
Ebdim (Bb Bass)
Ab (Bb Bass)
4th fret
Cm
Wait - ing at the
mp

Cm (B♭ Bass)
Cm (A Bass)
A♭
4th fret
G
sta - tion with a work - day wind a - blow - ing, I've got noth - ing to do
D7-9
G
but watch the pass - ers by.
Fm7
E♭ (G Bass)
Mir - rored in their fac - es I see frus - tra - tion grow - ing, and they
F♯dim
G
D.C. al Coda
don't see it show - ing. Why do I?

E♭ (B♭ Bass)
A♭ (B♭ Bass)
4th fret
Coda
Ped.
E♭
D♭6
Ped.
A♭ (C Bass)
4th fret
A♭
4th fret
E♭ (G Bass)
Fm7
E♭ (G Bass)
B7

C♯m
C♯m (B Bass)
C♯m (A♯ Bass)
I have of - ten asked my - self the rea - son for the sad -
mp
A
G♯
E♭7-9
- ness in a world where tears are just a lul -
G♯
F♯m7
- la - by. If there's an - y an -
E (G♯ Bass)
- swer, may - be love can end the mad - ness. May - be

Gdim
G#
not, oh, but we can on - ly try!
C#m
E7 (B Bass)
A
You've got to get up ev - 'ry morn - in' with a
p
mf
F#m
E (B Bass)
C#m
smile on your face and show the world all the love in your
F#7
E (G# Bass)
(add F#)
Am
(A# Bass)
F#7
A
heart. Then peo - ple gon - na treat you bet -

E (B Bass)
ter. You're gon- na find, yes, you will, that you're beau-
C7
F♯m7
- ti - ful, you're beau - ti - ful,
3
Gdim
you're beau - ti - ful as you feel.
E (B Bass)
A (B Bass)

E
E7 (D Bass)
A
(G♯ Bass) A
F♯m7
E (B Bass)
C♯m7
F♯7
E (G♯ Bass)
(add F♯) Am
F♯7 (A♯ Bass)
A
E (B Bass)
C7
F♯m7
Gdim
E (B Bass)
Repeat and fade out
Ped.
*

Beautiful

Words and Music by
CAROLE KING

B
A♯dim
B
noth - ing to do but watch the pass - ers by.
world where tears are just a lul - la - by.
Am
G
Mir - rored in their fac - es I see frus - tra - tion grow - ing And they
If there's an - y an - swer may - be love can end the mad - ness. May - be
A♯dim
B
D.C. al ⊕ Coda
don't see it show - ing. Why do I?
not, oh, but we can on - ly try.
⊕ Coda
Am7
B♭dim
you're beau - ti - ful, you're beau - ti - ful
G
Am7/D
G
as you feel.

where you lead

By Toni Stern and Carole King

Wanting you the way I do,
I only want to be with you,
And I would go to the ends of the earth,
'Cause, darlin', to me that's what you're worth.
Where you lead I will follow,
Anywhere that you tell me to.
If you need, need me to be with you,
I will follow where you lead.
If you're out on the road,
Feeling lonely and so cold,
All you gotta do is call my name
And I'll be there on the next train,
Where you lead I will follow,
Anywhere that you tell me to.
If you need, need me to be with you,
I will follow where you lead.
I always wanted a real home
With flowers on the window sill,
But if you want to live in New York City,
Honey, you know I will.
I never thought I could get satisfaction
From just one man,
But if anyone can keep me happy
You're the one who can.
Where you lead I will follow
Anywhere that you tell me to.
If you need, need me to be with you,
I will follow. Oh, where you lead
I will follow anywhere that you tell me to.
If you need, need me to be with you,
I will follow. Where you lead.
Where you lead I will follow.
Where you lead I will follow.

Where You Lead

Words and Music by
CAROLE KING and TONI STERN

C
F
(C Bass)
C
F
— I will fol - low, — an - y - where — that you tell —
C
F
(C Bass)
C
G
(B Bass)
Am
C7
(G Bass)
— me to. — If you need, — need me to be — with you, — I will fol-
Dm
Em
Dm
(F Bass)
F6
(G Bass)
C
F
C
low — where you lead. — I al - ways want-ed a real —
mf
F
C
— home — with flow- ers on the win - dow — sill, — but

F C F
if you want to live in New York City, honey, you know I will.
C F C
I never thought I could get satisfaction
F C F C
from just one man, but if anyone can keep
F Em Dm7 Dm7 (G Bass)
me happy, you're the one who can. Where you lead

C F C F
I will fol - low, an - y - where that you tell
C F (C Bass) C Em (B Bass) Am C7 (G Bass)
me to. If you need, need me to be with you, I will fol-
Dm Em Dm (F Bass) F (G Bass)
low. Oh, where you lead
Dm Em Dm (F Bass) F (G Bass)
- low where you lead.
C F (C Bass) C F (C Bass) C F C (E Bass) Dm C
Where you lead I will fol - low. Where you lead
Fade

Where You Lead

Words and Music by
CAROLE KING and TONI STERN

smackwater jack

By Gerry Goffin and Carole King

Now Smackwater Jack, he bought a shotgun
'Cause he was in the mood for a little confrontation.
He just a let it all hang loose,
He didn't think about the noose;
He couldn't take no more abuse,
So he shot down the congregation.
You can't talk to a man with a shotgun in his hand.
Now Big Jim, the chief, stood for law and order.
He called for the guard to come and surround the border.
From his bulldog mouth as he led the posse south,
Came the cry, ''We've got to ride to clean up the streets
For our wives and our daughters.''
You can't talk to a man with a shotgun in his hand.
The account of the capture wasn't in the papers,
But you know they hanged old Smack right there
Instead of later. You know the people were quite pleased
'Cause the outlaw had been seized
And on the whole it was a very good year for the undertaker.
You can't talk to a man with a shotgun in his hand,
A shotgun in his hand.
Smackwater Jack bought a shotgun. Yeah!
Smackwater Jack bought a shotfun. Yeah!

Smackwater Jack

Words and Music by
GERRY GOFFIN and CAROLE KING

D G D G D
mood for a lit-tle con - fron-ta - tion. He just - a'
guard to come and sur-round the bor - der.
Smack right there in - stead of lat - er. You know the
G7
let it all hang-loose, he did-n't think a-bout the noose;
From his bull - dog mouth, as he led the pos - se south,
peo-ple were quite pleased, 'cause the out - law had been seized.
A G
To Coda
he could-n't take no more a - buse, so he shot down the
came the cry, "We've got to ride to clean up the streets.
and on the whole it was a ver - y good year.
1.
D G D
(D Bass)
con - gre - ga - tion. You can't
3

A Bm A Bm7
talk to a man with a shot - gun in his
G G7
2.
hand. for our wives and our daugh-
D G D A Bm
(D Bass)
ters." You can't talk to a man
A Bm7 G
D.S. 𝄋 al ⊕ Coda
with a shot - gun in his hand.

G
D
G
(D Bass)
D
For the un - der - tak - er.
You can't
Coda
3
A
Bm
A
Bm7
G
talk to a man with a shot - gun in his hand,
a
G7
D
G
D
shot-gun in his hand.
Smack-wa-ter Jack bought a shot -
Repeat and fade
G
D
G
gun. Yeah! Smack-wa-ter Jack bought a shot - gun.

Smackwater Jack

Words and Music by
GERRY GOFFIN and CAROLE KING

tapestry

By Carole King

My life has been a tapestry of rich and royal hue,
An everlasting vision of the ever-changing views,
A wond'rous woven magic in bits of blue and gold,
Once amid the soft and silver sadness in the sky,
A tapestry to feel and see, impossible to hold.
There came a man of fortune, a drifter passing by.
He wore a torn and tattered cloth around his leathered hide
And a coat of many colors, yellow, green on either side.
He moved with some uncertainty as if he didn't know
Just what he was there for or where he ought to go.
Once he reached for something golden
Hanging from a tree and his hand came down empty.
Soon within my tapestry along the rutted road,
He sat down on a river rock and turned into a toad.
It seemed that the had fallen into someone's wicked spell.
I wept to see him suffer, though I didn't know him well.
As I watched in sorrow there suddenly appeared
A figure grey and ghostly beneath a flowing beard.
In times of deepest darkness I've seen him dressed in black.
Now my tapestry's unravelling; he's come to take me back.
He's come to take me back.

Tapestry

Words and Music by
CAROLE KING

Slowly (In Two)

F
Gm7
C
Gm7
(D Bass)
Gm7
view, a wond - 'rous wov - en mag - ic in bits of blue and gold,
C
B♭
Am7
Gm7
a tap - es - try to feel and see im - pos - si - ble to hold.
C
Fmaj7
(C Bass)
B♭
Once, a - mid the soft, sil - ver
Soon, with - in my tap - es - try, a -
mf
Fmaj7
(C Bass)
B♭
Fmaj7
sad - ness in the sky, there came a man of for -
long the rut - ted road, he sat down on a
Ped. *

(C Bass)
Bb
Fmaj7
Bb(F Bass)
F
tune, a drift - er pass - ing by. He
riv-er rock and turned in - to a toad. It
Gm7
C
Gm7
wore a torn and tat - tered cloth a - round his leath - ered hide,
seemed that he had fal - len in - to some - one's wick - ed spell,
C
Bbmaj7
Am7
3
and a coat of man - y col - ors, yel-low
and I wept to see him suf - er, though I
Gm7
C
Gm7
C
To Coda
green on eith - er side. He
did-n't know him

A♭ (A♭ Bass) D♭ (A♭ Bass) E♭ (A♭ Bass) D♭
moved with some un - cer - tain - ty, as if he did - n't know
A♭ (A♭ Bass) D♭ (A♭ Bass) E♭ (A♭ Bass) D♭ A♭
just what he was there for, or where he ought to go.
C (C Bass) G (C Bass) F
Once he reached for some-thing gold - en, hang - ing from a tree,
C (F Bass) C (B♭ Bass) C B♭maj7 B♭ F Gm7
and his hand came down emp - ty.
D.S. 𝄋 al ⊕ Coda
mp

C
F♯
(add 9)
B(F♯ Bass)
well. As I watched in sor - row, there
Coda
f
(add 9)
B(F♯ Bass)
F♯
sud - den - ly ap - peared a fig - ure, grey and
(add 9)
B(F♯ Bass)
F♯
(F♯ Bass)
B
F♯
ghost - ly, be - neath a flow - ing beared. In
mp
G♯m7
C♯
G♯m7
times of deep - est dark - ness, I've seen him dressed in

C♯
Bmaj7
B♭m7
G♯m7
rall.
black. Now my tap - es-try's un - rav - el - ing; he's come to take me
rall.
Slower Tempo
(D♯ Bass)
C♯
G♯m7
C♯
rall.
back. He's come to take me back.
rall.
(add 9)
B (C♯ Bass)
accel.
F♯
B (F♯ Bass)
Tempo I
accel.
mf
(C♯ Bass)
F♯
B (F♯ Bass)
F♯ (C♯ Bass)
B
C♯7
F♯
rall.

Tapestry

Words and Music by
CAROLE KING

E♭ B♭7sus E♭ A♭ E♭ G
Just what he was there for or where he ought to go. Once he reached for
D C G C
some - thing gold - en hang - ing from a tree And his hand came down
F N.C. F C Dm7 C G7sus
emp - ty.
Soon with - in my tap - es - try a -
As I watched in sor - row there
C G7sus C G7sus C F
long the rut - ted road, He sat down on a riv - er rock and turned in - to a
sud - den - ly ap - peared A fig - ure gray and ghost - ly be - neath a flow - ing
C Dm7 G Dm7 G
toad. It seemed that he had fal - len in - to some - one's wick - ed spell. I
beard. In times of deep - est dark - ness I've seen him dressed in black. Now my
F C Dm7 1. G 2. G
wept to see him suf - fer, though I did - n't know him well.
tap - es - try's un - rav - el - ling; he's come to take me back.

(you make me feel like) a natural woman

By Carole King, Gerry Goffin and Jerry Wexler

Lookin' out on the morning rain
I used to feel uninspired
And when I knew I'd have to face another day,
Lord, it made me feel so tired.
Before the day I met you life was so unkind.
Your love was the key to my peace of mind
'Cause you make me feel, you make me feel,
You make me feel like a natural woman
When my soul was in the lost and found
You came along to claim it.
I didn't know what was wrong with me
Till your kiss helped me name it.
Now I'm no longer doubtful of what I'm livin' for
'Cause if I make you happy I don't need to do more.
You make me feel, you make me feel,
You make me feel, like a natural woman.
Oh, baby, what you've done to me!
(What you've done to me!)
You make me feel so good inside. (Good inside.)
And I just want to be (want to be) close to you.
You make me feel so alive!
You make me feel, you make me feel,
You make me feel like a natural, natural woman.
You make me feel, you make me feel,
You make me feel like a natural woman,
A natural woman.

(You Make Me Feel Like) A Natural Woman

Words and Music by
GERRY GOFFIN, CAROLE KING
and JERRY WEXLER

A
(C♯ Bass)
Bm7
C♯m7
Before the day I met you,
life was so unkind.
Dmaj7
(E Bass)
Your love was the key to my peace of mind,
'cause you make me feel,
D
you make me feel,
you make me feel like a

A D A (C♯ Bass) Bm7 Bm7 (E Bass) to Coda A
nat - u - ral wo - man. When my
E (G♯ Bass) G
soul was in the lost and found, you came a -
D A (C♯ Bass) Bm7 A
long to claim it. I did - n't
E (G♯ Bass) G
know just what was wrong with me, 'til your

D
A
(C♯ Bass)
Bm7
kiss helped me name it. Now I'm no long - er
C♯m7
Bm7
C♯m7
doubt - ful ___ of what I'm liv - in' for, 'cause
Bm7
C♯m7
Dmaj7
D.S. 𝄋 al ⊕ Coda
if I make you hap - py I don't need to do ___ more. ___
A
G
(A Bass)
⊕ Coda
Oh, ___ ba - by, what you've done to me! ___ (What you've

D
A
done to me!)
You make me feel so good
G
(A Bass)
in - side.
(Good in - side.)
Dmaj7
Am7
(D Bass)
And I just want to be
(want to be)
D
A
(C♯ Bass)
Bm7
close to you. You make me feel so a - live!
You

Bm7
(E Bass)
A
Dmaj7
make me feel, You make me
A
Dmaj7
A D A
(C♯ Bass)
A D6 A6
(C♯ Bass)
feel, You make me feel like a nat - u - ral,
Bm7
1.2.
Bm7
(E Bass)
Bm7
3.
nat - u - ral wo - man. You make me wo - man, a
Bm7
(E Bass)
A
D A
(C♯ Bass)
Bm7 A
nat - u - ral wo - man.

(You Make Me Feel Like) A Natural Woman

Words and Music by
GERRY GOFFIN, CAROLE KING
and JERRY WEXLER

Printed in England
The Panda Group · Haverhill · Suffolk · 1/98